MIDNIGHT FOREST

MIDNIGHT FOREST

and other poems

Judith Nicholls

faber and faber

LONDON · BOSTON

First published in 1987
by Faber and Faber Limited
3 Queen Square London WC1N 3AU

Photoset and printed in Great Britain by
Redwood Burn Limited, Trowbridge, Wiltshire
All rights reserved

British Library Cataloguing in Publication Data

Nicholls, Judith
Midnight Forest and other poems.
I. Title
823'.914[J]   PZ7

ISBN 0–571–14807–7

Midnight Forest and *The Experiment* first appeared
in the Schools' Poetry Association's *Poetry Express*.
Season Song and *Winter* were broadcast on the
BBC Schools Radio programme *Living Language*
and appeared in the accompanying notes.

for John,
with love

CONTENTS

MIDNIGHT FOREST

Who wanders wild
in moon and puffball light
where night sleeps black
and spiders creep?
What is that sound
that stills the air?
Whose is the breath
that rustles oak and fir?
Beware,
the tree-gods stir.

SUPERSTITIONS

Wash your hands in the moonlight,
don't step on any crack;
cross your fingers,
cross your toes,
touch wood to keep your luck.

Always watch for black cats,
wear odd socks unawares;
choose sevens or threes,
'Bless you!' when you sneeze,
and never cross on stairs.

Remember these with all you've got;
                                    if not . . .

WITCH'S CAT

is noiseless,
felt at dark
like silent breath;
stalker, not stalked,
a leaf or web
that brushes flesh,
the creak of empty stairs,
the cloud that darkens stars
and shrouds a moon.

Witch's cat
like fear, runs wild,
child of the shadows;
no child of light,
this silent cat of night.

CAT

My cat's tail
can dance or beckon
whilst he sleeps,
can wave or threaten,
fall or rise.

Warily
it lies awake,
all on its own;
he wakes,
it lies forgotten.
It lives a life alone,
quite separate –
or so it seems.

Could it be the place
where, secretly,
his life goes on?
A space to hide for ever
a million catty dreams?

DOG

Best friend?
Maybe!
Wiry hair-dropper,
four-legged yapper.
Sleep-disturber,
paws on the shoulders
and lick on the chin.
Unruly friend, sometimes.
I remember
Great Dane,
lolloping up stairs,
five-at-a-time
then sitting,
patient King of the Castle,
waiting for his slow
two-legged servant,
panting below.
Best friend!

WHO'S THERE?

Knock, knock!
Who's there?
cried the spider.
Stand and wait!
But she knew by the
gentle tweak of the web
it was her mate.

Knock, knock!
Who's there?
cried the spider.
Call your name!
But she knew by the
soft tap-tap on the silk
her spiderlings came.

Knock, knock!
Who's there?
cried the spider.
Who goes by?
But she knew by the
shaking of her net
it was the fly.

WOODLOUSE

Armoured dinosaur,
blundering through jungle grass by
dandelion-light.

Knight's headpiece, steel-hinged
orange-segment, ball-bearing,
armadillo-drop.

Pale peppercorn, pearled
eyeball; sentence without end,
my rolling full-stop.

TIGER

Tiger, eyes dark with
half-remembered forest night,
stalks an empty cage.

WOLF

still on his lone rock
stares at the uncaged stars and
cries into the night.

DEAR NOAH . . .

Moth

One corner of the ark –
a mulberry leaf to fly on,
lay on, eat from, lie on;
and please, a firefly, just one,
to dance around at dark.

Sloth

I like this floating bed –
the warm smell of animal,
a log to swing on
as the clouds drift by.
Supper is brought
and all day long
the seagull-cry
and sigh of lapping waves,
my lullaby.

Worm

Give me a hole to slither in,
rain for wallowing, soil for swallowing
and not too many fishermen with hooks.

Please, Noah.

TORTOISE AND HARE POEM

(or: Slow, slow, quick, quick, slow . . .)

Slowly the tortoise raised her head,
stared slowly at the hare;
slowly stepped towards the line
and waited there.

Calmly she heard the starting gun,
crawled calmly down the track;
calmly watched the hare race on
with arching back.

Quickly the hare ran out of sight,
chased quickly through the wood;
quickly fled through fern and moss,
through leaf and mud.

Swiftly he leapt past hedge and field,
sped swiftly for his prize;
briefly stopped to take a rest –
and closed his eyes.

Slowly the tortoise reached the wood,
slowly she ambled on.
The hare raced proudly through his dreams;
the tortoise won.

READY, STEADY? NO!

My Dad's
a keep-fit fiend.
You know,

press-ups and sit-ups,
jogging and squash;
toe-touch and leg-stretch,
lunch on the dash.
No time for an old-fashioned
ploughman's and beer,
'The pool's open now,
we can sprint it from here!'

Even on Sundays
he's up with the lark:
tennis in summer,
weights after dark.
Arms bend and neck twist,
runs on the spot,
scissor-jumps, rugby –
he does the lot.

As for me,
I *hate* sport,
prefer bed until three;
a mere game of draughts
is exhausting to me.
He'll always hike;
well, I'll join the queue
and travel by train,
as we were meant to!

SISTER

Tell me a story!
Lend me that book!
Please, let me come in your den?
I won't mess it up,
so *please* say I can.
When? When? When?

Lend me that engine,
that truck – and your glue.
I'll give half of my old bubblegum.
You know what Dad said
about learning to share.
Give it *now* –
or I'm telling Mum!

Oh, *please* lend your bike –
I'll be careful this time.
I'll keep out of the mud
and the snow.
I could borrow your hat –
the one you've just got . . .

                said my sister.

And I said

        NO!

ADVICE

Do put a coat on,
and fasten that shoe.
I'd take a sweater,
      if I were you . . .

It's chilly at nights now,
you're bound to catch 'flu;
I'd button up warmly,
      if I were you . . .

Please yourself if you must
but I know what *I'd* do;
I'd stay at home now,
      if I were you . . .

The nights have drawn in,
you never know who
might be lurking out there
      just waiting for you . . .

I don't know what the youth
of today's coming to!
They do what they like
      and like what they do!

Now when *I* was young,
it caused hullaballoo
if I stayed out past nine –
      and I never dared to.

If I were young now,
I know what *I'd* do . . .

I'd enjoy every minute
if I were you!

MUM AND DAD...

Weather wet,
food bad;
send cash
please Dad.

Sick on coach
(only twice)
Bill shares tent
(got headlice).

Field's a bog,
full of flies;
local bull
quite a size.

Wellies pinched,
sweaters gone;
walked to town
on my own.

Sir still drunk,
fell in bin –
by the way,
I like gin!

Enjoy your rest,
have a ball,
relaxez-vous
one and all.

Better stop,
doing the town.

See you soon,
love from John.

p.s.   *Forget cash,*
raid's on!
Must dash –
loving son.

xxxxxxx

I'M A VEGGIE

The day my Mum
went vegetarian
we ate

cabbage and carrot
and juicy nut stew,
peanut and chestnut,
pistachio, cashew;
yoghurt with honey,
sesame thins,
peas, beans and pumpkin
(out went the tins!)
Dates, grapes, bananas,
lentils, cheese pie,
potatoes, tomatoes . . .
We thought we would die
without our chip fix,
our sausage and mash,
greasy bacon, beefburgers,
thick cornbeef hash . . .

Funny thing was,
she went off for a week.
'Quick, the butcher!' cried Dad,
keen to give us a treat.
We stuffed ourselves silly
on turkey and ham,
on roast beef and gravy
and pink fatty Spam;
bacon with breakfast,
lamb's leg for lunch,
pork scratchings for snacks

when we needed a munch.
After six days of that . . .

We just couldn't wait
for a huge pile of beetroot
and prunes on our plate!
We forgot about beef
and all made solemn pledges
from that day to this
to be long-crunching veggies!

RUSH HOUR

Nine o'clock,
the bell has gone!
Walk in quietly;
Tim, lead on . . . . . .

And the whole of Class Four
make a dash for the door:
scuttle and scurry,
hurtle and flurry,
jotter and tostle,
stragger and hastle;
muscle and bolting,
bolliding and sholting,
beap, sweep and jumble,
shunt, shove and trundle,
swallop and chase . . .
You'd never have guessed
from the way that they race

they all HATE SCHOOL!

NICE WORK

Never use the word NICE,
                our teacher said.
It doesn't mean a thing!
Try . . .
beautiful, shining, delicious,
shimmering, hopeful, auspicious,
attractive, unusual, nutritious –
the choice is as long as a string!
But please, *never* use the word NICE,
it just doesn't mean a thing!

(*She's nice, our teacher.*)

BULLY

Slowly he straightened his back,
ran chewed stumps through his hair;

slowly he straightened leathered knees
and got up from his chair.

Slowly he fixed me with his eye
(I dared not leave his glare);

slowly he reached to his pocket,
put something there.

Slowly he stepped towards me,
his mouth curled in a grin;

slowly, slowly, he came closer . . .
Quickly . . . I RAN!

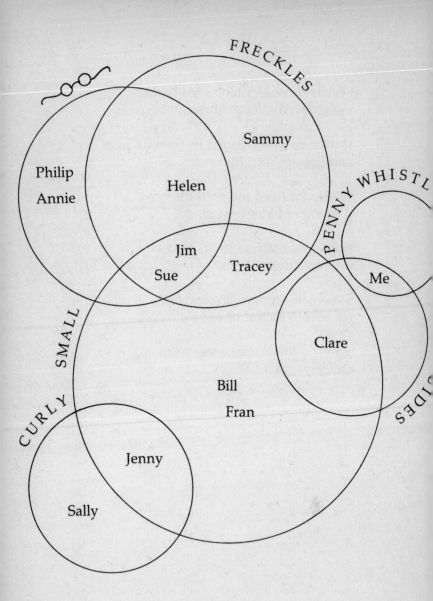

FRECKLES

PENNY WHISTL

Sammy

Philip
Annie

Helen

Jim
Sue

Tracey

Me

CURLY SMALL

Clare

Bill
Fran

IDES

Jenny

Sally

CLASSIFYING

Philip and Annie wear glasses
and so do Jim and Sue,
but Jim and Sue have freckles,
and Tracey and Sammy too.
Philip and Jim are in boys' group
but Philip is tall like Sam
whilst Jim is small like Tracey and Sue
and Clare and Bill and Fran.
Sue is in Guides and Recorders,
but Clare is in Guides and football
whilst Helen fits in most things –
except she's a girl and quite tall.
Jenny is curly and blonde and short
whilst Sally is curly but dark;
Jenny likes netball, writing and maths
but Sally likes no kind of work.
Philip and Sam are both jolly,
Fran's best for a quiet chat;
now I
        have freckles, like joking, am tall,
        curly, dark, in Guides, football and
        play penny whistles and the piano . . .

how do *I* fit into all that?

THE EXPERIMENT

I want you to think,
said sir,
about *nothing*,
sir said.
Empty your head;
sit dead still,
don't move a toe
until I say so.
Ready? – *Go!*

It's easy not to blink –
you'd think.
First I blinked.
Then I saw Gary Flynn
pinching his lips
to keep the giggle in.
My big toe wiggled,
Kevin Nuttall wriggled,
Mary Bollom sneezed,
the clown!
I could see sir
trying hard to frown
without moving his face.
I squeezed my toes,
Kevin Nuttall froze
and Mary Bollom went red.
I tried hard to sit still
and c-o-n-c-e-n-t-r-a-t-e
as *nothing*
rushed through my head.

PARTNERS

Find a partner,
says sir, and sit
with him or her.
A whisper here,
a shuffle there,
a rush of feet.
One pair,
another pair,
till twenty-four
sit safely on the floor
and all are gone
but one
who stands,
like stone,
and waits;
tall,
still,

alone.

THE DARE

Go on, I dare you,
come on down!

Was it *me* they called?
Pretend you haven't heard,
a voice commanded in my mind.
Walk past, walk fast
and don't look down,
don't look behind.

Come on, it's easy!

The banks were steep,
the water low
and flanked with oozing brown.
Easy? Walk fast
but don't look down.
Walk straight, walk on,
even risk their jeers
and run . . .

Never go near those dykes,
my mother said.
No need to tell me.
I'd seen stones sucked in
and covered without trace,
gulls slide to bobbing safety,
grasses drown as water rose.
No need to tell me
to avoid the place.

She ca-a-a-n't, she ca-a-a-n't!

Cowardy, cowardy custard!

There's no such word as 'can't',
my father said.
I slowed my pace.
The voices stopped,
waited as I wavered, grasping breath.
My mother's wrath? My father's scorn?
A watery death?

I hesitated then turned back,
forced myself to see the mud below.
After all, it was a dare . . .
There was no choice;
I had to go.

VILLAGE SCHOOL

A stile, a field,
some dozen cows
and then the church.
A muddy dyke,
some silver roach
and just below the bridge
a sharp-toothed pike
which lurks alone
for small unwary stragglers,
whispering doom.

The school, one room.
Beneath high-windowed stone
fixed smiling in her chair
the kindly Mrs Mullins,
large in blue and black
with neatly-curlered hair.
From nine to twelve
and later on till three
she calls our fate
and welcomes all
on ample knee.
A scratch of slate,
a shuffle here or there,
a child in late;
chalk-dusted autumn
clouds the air.

At last a break. Wait
unwillingly for bottled milk,
cool in its rattling crate,
then under teacher's watchful eye

lace-up for play.
Scarves, coats and hopscotch
when the weather's dry
and crying at the gate for home
under a grey Lincolnshire sky.

A LINCOLNSHIRE
NURSERY RHYME

Boston, Wainfleet,
Haxey, Hogsthorpe, Well;
Weston, Westborough,
Thorpe, Brigg, Hale.

Old Leake and Mumby,
Osbournby, Fleet,
Old Bolingbroke, Leverton,
Bourne, Lea, Wroot.

POACHED EGG

Huttoft, Dunsby, Sapperton, Well,
Haxey, Dowsby, Hacconby, Haugh;
Addlethorpe, Harrington, Asgarby, Waith,
Cumberworth, Holdingham, Gautby, Lea, Knaith.

BIKING

Fingers grip,
toes curl;
head down,
wheels whirl.

Hair streams,
fields race;
ears sting,
winds chase.

Breathe deep,
troubles gone;
just feel
windsong.

SONG OF THE FROG PRINCE

It's the royal bed I miss.
Oh, I can do without
the state occasions,
the bowing and the handshakes,
the gold crown, weighting my head.
All those unwanted presents
to be grateful for,
and far too many strawberries,
out-of-season.
But the royal bed . . .
pillows, soft with silk,
deep, feathered mattresses
with satin sheets,
quilts billowing with eider.

A kiss, dear lady, please.
Just one small kiss.

DAVID AND GOLIATH

David was a shepherd boy,
Jesse's youngest son;
watched his sheep,
played his harp,
practised with his sling.
He learned to cast a pebble
through the mountain air;
a loin cloth was his armour.
From lion, jackal, bear
he rescued Jesse's sheep alone.
He knew no fear.

His king was Saul,
a brave one
who kept the Philistines at bay;
bold in battle any day,
he later came to disobey
and was undone.

Saul, Saul,
your mood is black;
call for the boy
with the magic harp.

The shepherd boy lay dreaming
in the summer grass
when they called him to the palace
to help Saul's dark dreams pass.
His music calmed the troubled king
who smiled to hear his song;
but meantime
on the mountainside
the Philistines marched on.

Saul, Saul,
your champion please
to fight our giant, fast!

Across the valley
stood Goliath,
bristling, vast.

Goliath rang,
an iron man:
helmet, brass,
coat of mail,
breastplate, legplates,
spear and shield.
Ten feet tall,
spearshaft wide
as any arm
on that mountainside.

I'll fight this man,
said David.
King Saul was full of doubt
but they set him up in plates of brass,
quite sure that he had breathed his last
and sent him out.

The shepherd boy
took off his mail,
took off his shield and sword.
I fought a lion with God's help,
I'm safe with just His word.
Goliath is no jackal
though he hides in a coat of mail,
and might's not right

in every fight;
I shall not fail.

Goliath looked. He stared.
He laughed. He roared.
His legplates shook,
his army cheered.

Goliath jeered

I'll give your flesh
to the fowls of the air,
your heart
to the beasts of the field;
your liver will fill
some roaming bear
when I've wiped you
off my shield!
Where is your sword,
vile midget?
Are you really
the best they could find?
Step forward,
let's finish this quickly!
I'll grind your bones
like summer wheat
and scatter your chaff
to the wind!

But David stood.

He heard the Philistines' laughter,
he heard Goliath's jeer;
the giant's metal music rang
discordant in his ear.

He picked five stones
from a nearby stream;
swung one, flung one, stood . . .
it arched like Noah's rainbow
then caught the giant's head.
He fell like a dove to the mountainside.
His army scattered like chaff as they cried
Goliath's dead!

David was a shepherd boy,
Jesse's youngest son;
slew Goliath,
saved his country –
with a stone.

JONAH'S LAMENT

Dark, only dark,
with only hands for eyes;
saved – for a life of touch!
Is *this* my end,
fumbling at some bony stalactite
inside this dank, rank cave?
What scaffold props my roof,
curves out damp walls,
all velvet-hung?
Moist flesh,
indenting to my touch,
closes like giant clam,
a curling tongue.
Some swallowed, mucus-tacky fish
noses its scaly length about my neck,
lost in the slap of falling sea.
Salt rinses mouth and lips
and all around the stench
of half-digested fish
breathes over me.

PERSEPHONE

Lay down your poppies
   red with sun,
   beneath the judas-tree;
   beware the black-horsed lord of night,
   Persephone.

Bury your violets
   with the shades,
   drink deep the black, black sea;
   ferry your corn to Dis's cave,
   Persephone.

Fasten your veil with
   lilies pale,
   dull nightshade dim your eyes;
   under sad lilac make your grave,
   till winter dies.

STORYTIME

Once upon a time, children,
there lived a fearsome dragon . . .

Please, miss,
Jamie's made a dragon.
Out in the sandpit.

Lovely, Andrew.
Now this dragon
had enormous red eyes
and a swirling, whirling tail . . .

Jamie's dragon's got
yellow eyes, miss.

Lovely, Andrew.
Now this dragon was
as wide as a horse
as green as the grass
as tall as a house . . .

Jamie's would JUST fit
in our classroom, miss!

But he was a very friendly dragon . . .

Jamie's dragon ISN'T, miss.
He eats people, miss.
Especially TEACHERS,
Jamie said.

Very nice, Andrew!

Now one day, children,
this enormous dragon
rolled his red eye,
whirled his swirly green tail
and set off to find . . .

His dinner, miss!
Because he was hungry, miss!

Thank you, Andrew.
He rolled his red eye,
whirled his green tail,
and opened his wide, wide mouth
until

> *Please, miss,*
> *I did try to tell you, miss!*

LEARNING TO SWIM

Today I am
dolphin-over-the-waves,
roach and stickleback,
silver mermaid,
turning tide,
ribbon-weed
or sprat.

Water drifts through my mind;
I twist, I glide,
leave fear behind in sand,
wander a land
of turtle, minnow, seal
where whale is king.

Today – I swim!

SEA DREAM

I wander the deep-sea forests
where the snake-fish slither;
where the dark dunes drift
like rolling mist
and the white whales murmur.

I wake to coral blossom
and sleep in a star-clad cave;
my bed is a glade
of ribboned jade,
my sky a wave.

I dance by the spiny urchin
and ride the giant clam;
I feel as I sail
the dolphin's tail
the sad whale song.

MARY CELESTE

Only the wind sings
in the riggings,
the hull creaks a lullaby;
a sail lifts gently
like a message
pinned to a vacant sky.
The wheel turns
over bare decks,
shirts flap on a line;
only the song of the lapping waves
beats steady time . . .

First mate,
off-duty from
the long dawn watch, begins
a letter to his wife, daydreams
of home.

The Captain's wife is late;
the child did not sleep
and breakfast has passed . . .
She, too, is missing home;
sits down at last to eat,
but can't quite force
the porridge down.
She swallows hard,
slices the top from her egg.

The second mate
is happy.
A four-hour sleep,
full stomach
and a quiet sea

are all he craves.
He has all three.

Shirts washed and hung, beds
made below, decks done, the boy
stitches a torn sail.

The Captain
has a good ear for a tune;
played his child to sleep
on the ship's organ.
Now, music left,
he checks his compass,
lightly tips the wheel,
hopes for a westerly.
Clear sky, a friendly sea,
fair winds for Italy.

The child now sleeps, at last,
head firmly pressed into her pillow
in a deep sea-dream.

Then why are the gulls wheeling
like vultures in the sky?
Why was the child snatched
from her sleep? What drew
the Captain's cry?

Only the wind replies
in the rigging,
and the hull creaks and sighs;
a sail spells out its message
over silent skies.
The wheel still turns
over bare decks,

shirts blow on the line;
the siren-song of lapping waves
still echoes over time.

A POEM FOR THE RAINFOREST

Song of the Xingu Indian

They have stolen my land;
the birds have flown,
my people gone.
My rainbow rises over sand,
my river falls on stone.

        Amazonian Timbers, Inc.

        This can go next –
        here, let me draw the line.
        That's roughly right,
        give or take
        a few square miles or so.
        I'll list the ones we need.
        No, burn the rest.
        Only take the best,
        we're not in this
        for charity.
        Replant? No –
        you're new to this, I see!
        There's plenty more
        where that comes from,
        no problem! Finish here –
        and then move on.

Dusk

Butterfly, blinded
by smoke, drifts like torn paper
to the flames below.

Shadows

Spider,
last of her kind,
scuttles underground, safe;
prepares her nest for young ones. But
none come.

The Coming of Night

Sun sinks
behind the high canopy;
the iron men are silenced.

The moon rises,
the firefly wakes.
Death pauses for a night.

Song of the Forest

*Our land has gone,
our people flown.
Sun scorches our earth,
our river weeps.*

SEASON SONG

Spring stirs slowly, shuffles, hops;
Summer dances close behind.
Autumn is a jostling crowd
but Winter creeps into your mind.

DANDELION IN WINTER

Where now, my
sleepyhead, old lion's teeth,
bold wet-the-bed?
Sly stowaway, why hide away
your golden wine
till leafy May?
No mirrored stars
for chill December fields?
Where did it go,
your time-tell summer snow
now winter's come?
Your molten suns
lie buried, cold
and yet . . .
you whisper
from your silent world,
volcano-rumbles
caging summer power.
A thousand traitors
lurk in earth's damp cellar,
wait till March gives in;
then every spring . . .
You win, you win, you win!
My phantom sower,
sparkler-shower,
heart-of-iron,
dandelion!

WINTER

Winter crept
through the whispering wood,
hushing fir and oak;
crushed each leaf and froze each web –
but never a word he spoke.

Winter prowled
by the shivering sea,
lifting sand and stone;
nipped each limpet silently –
and then moved on.

Winter raced
down the frozen stream,
catching at his breath;
on his lips were icicles,
at his back was death.

ROOM AT THE INN

Draughty, husband, that stable.
She looked . . . warm, though.
Almost at home.
And you know, husband, I swear
it's not one mite as dark in there
as you'd have thought.
And that child – so still, so quiet.
Perhaps they'll need more straw?
It won't get any warmer, early hours.
Maybe we should bring them in?
Husband, you're not listening!

There is our bed . . .
but then with breakfast early
and so many travellers . . .
Well, *they* won't go tomorrow, surely?
Husband, did you see . . .?
Husband!
Oh well, old man, dream on!
Some day we've had,
and then those two arriving,
with every nook and cranny gone!

Funny how those moths
circled the old lantern,
husband. Almost like . . .
almost as if those three . . .
but no, it couldn't be!
And the light,
you should have seen the light!
Oh, it flickered, but
so bright, so bright,

and night so still.
Draughty it is, that stable,
husband.

DECEMBER

W   ater

I   ces

N   aked

T   rees;

E   arth

R   ests.